Welcome to Radiator Springs! We might be off the beaten path, but there's a whole lot going on in our small town. Cruise around and see if you can spot these cars who live here.

**Doc Hudson**

**Lizzie**

**Guido**

**Ramone**

**Flo**

**Mater**

Welcome to Flo's V8 Cafe. There are always plenty of treats to keep your engine a-purring and your tires a-turning. See if you can find these motor-watering morsels.

**Ice Cold Coolant**

**Mouthwatering Motor Oil**

**Transmission fluid**

**Wiper fluid**

**Anti-Freeze Frosty**

**Car wax**

Lightning McQueen might think he's the only race car in town, but Doc Hudson, the town doctor and judge, has a secret past. He was once a Piston Cup champ! Try to find these memories of Doc's racing days that are hidden in his garage.

**Blue ribbon**

**Plaque**

**Newspaper article**

**Flag**

**Antenna ball**

**Book**

Welcome to Lizzie's curios shop. Here you can buy sentimental souvenirs that will remind you of Radiator Springs for years to come. Try to find these fancy license plates.

8675309

A. STUDENT

NO. 1 DAD

HI MOM

I ❤ U

GO GO GO

Fantastico! Here we are at Luigi's tire shop, where the cars of Radiator Springs get fitted for new tires. See if you can spot some of Luigi's favorite brands.

**Fettuccini Crema**

**Fettuccini Blanco Maximo**

**Fettuccini Latte**

**Gripwell Tires**

**Tread Star**

**Welcome to the Radiator Springs Courthouse. There is a lot of history here, and most of it has to do with the town's founder, Stanley. See if you can find him in these portraits.**

Thank you for stopping by Radiator Springs. Can you find these postcards that will help you remember your visit?

**Flo's cafe**

**Doc Hudson's clinic**

**Mater's junkyard**

**Lizzie's curios shop**

**Luigi's shop**

**Courthouse**

Today is Nemo's first day of school. He and his father Marlin meet the teacher, Mr. Ray, at the schoolyard. Oh no, Nemo has wandered off with some of his classmates! Can you locate Nemo, his new school chums, their parents, and Mr. Ray in all the hustle and bustle?

Nemo

Pearl

Ted

Phil

Sheldon

Bob

Tad

Mr. Ray

**N**emo wandered too far away and is captured by a human diver! Marlin and his new friend, Dory, go into dangerous waters to look for clues that will help them find Nemo. Keep an eye out for these dangerous-looking sharks skulking about in the underwater minefield. Will Marlin and Dory make it through safely?

Bruce

Chum

Anchor

A basking shark

A sand shark

A whale shark

A tiger shark

**N**emo is placed into a fish tank. As it turns out, the diver who caught him is actually a dentist who loves fish! But life in an aquarium is not much fun. Help Nemo and the other fish in the tank pass the time by finding all these things in the dentist's waiting room:

*Dentists' Daily* newspaper

A tooth mug

A fish painting

Swedish fish

Fish crackers

A fish lunch box

A rainbow fish

BRUSH 'EM UP!

SWEDISH FISH

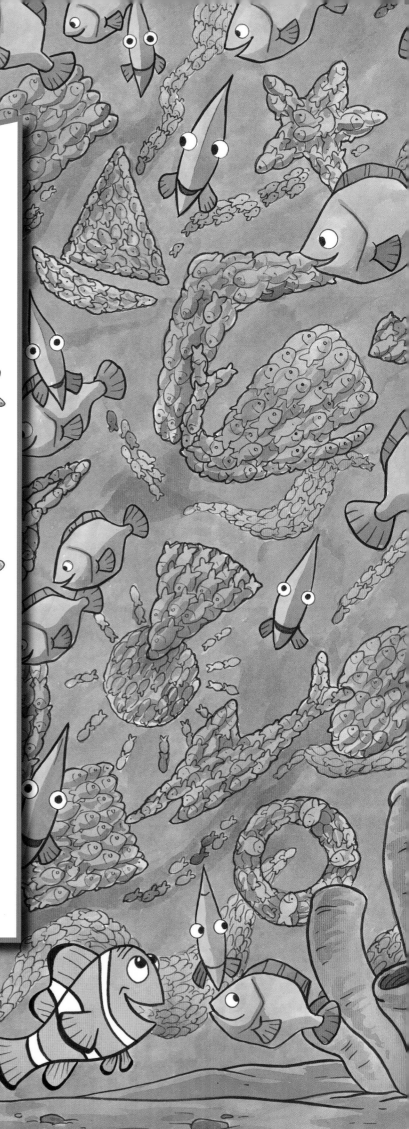

There is an address on a diver's mask Marlin and Dory find near the sub: "P. Sherman, 42 Wallaby Way, Sydney." But how will they get there when they can barely read? Some helpful moonfish make quite an "impression" by pointing the pair in the right direction. Can you help Marlin and Dory spot these other impressive moonfish signs?

"Octopus"

"Swordfish"

"Shark"

"Sea turtle"

"Starfish"

"Lobster"

"Whale"

Marlin and Dory meet up with a group of friendly turtles, including Crush and his son Squirt. They're all cruising down the East Australian Current, which should drop them off right by Sydney! See if you can scope out Crush, Squirt, and these other gnarly, shelled dudes!

Squirt

Crush

Flora

Checkers

Noelle

Target

Sydney

Pelé

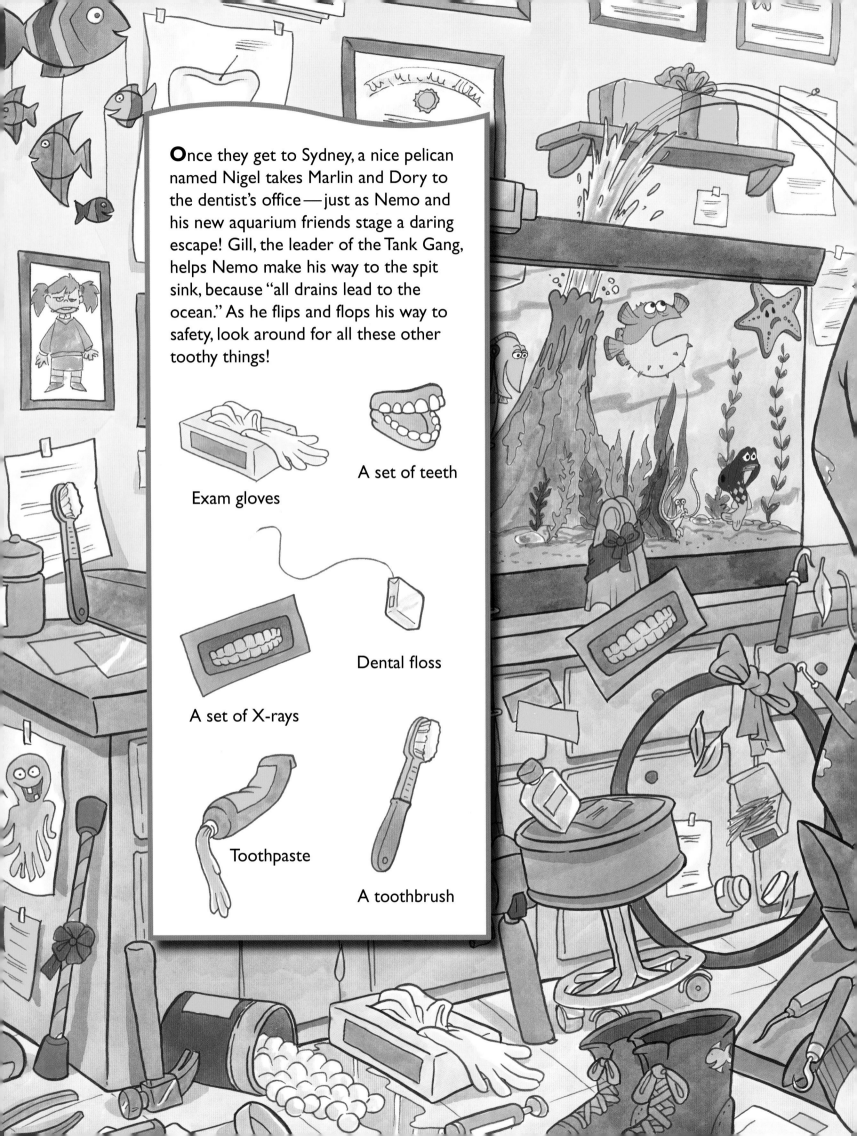

Once they get to Sydney, a nice pelican named Nigel takes Marlin and Dory to the dentist's office—just as Nemo and his new aquarium friends stage a daring escape! Gill, the leader of the Tank Gang, helps Nemo make his way to the spit sink, because "all drains lead to the ocean." As he flips and flops his way to safety, look around for all these other toothy things!

Exam gloves

A set of teeth

A set of X-rays

Dental floss

Toothpaste

A toothbrush

**B**ack in the ocean, again, Marlin and Nemo are reunited at last—but the excitement is not over yet! The two clownfish help a netful of fish pull off an escape of their own from some local fishermen. Now the grateful groupers are showering the pair with thanks! Can you find Marlin, Nemo, and these other fish in this seaworthy celebration?

Marlin

Nemo

This grouper

Dory

This grouper

This grouper

# WELCOME TO MONSTROPOLIS!

I'm Mike Wazowski, and this is top scarer, James P. Sullivan. Come with Sulley and me to Monsters, Inc. Safety is important, so remember – there is nothing more dangerous than a human child!

BRING YOUR LITTLE **MONSTER** TO WORK DAY!

TODAY AT MONSTERS, INC.

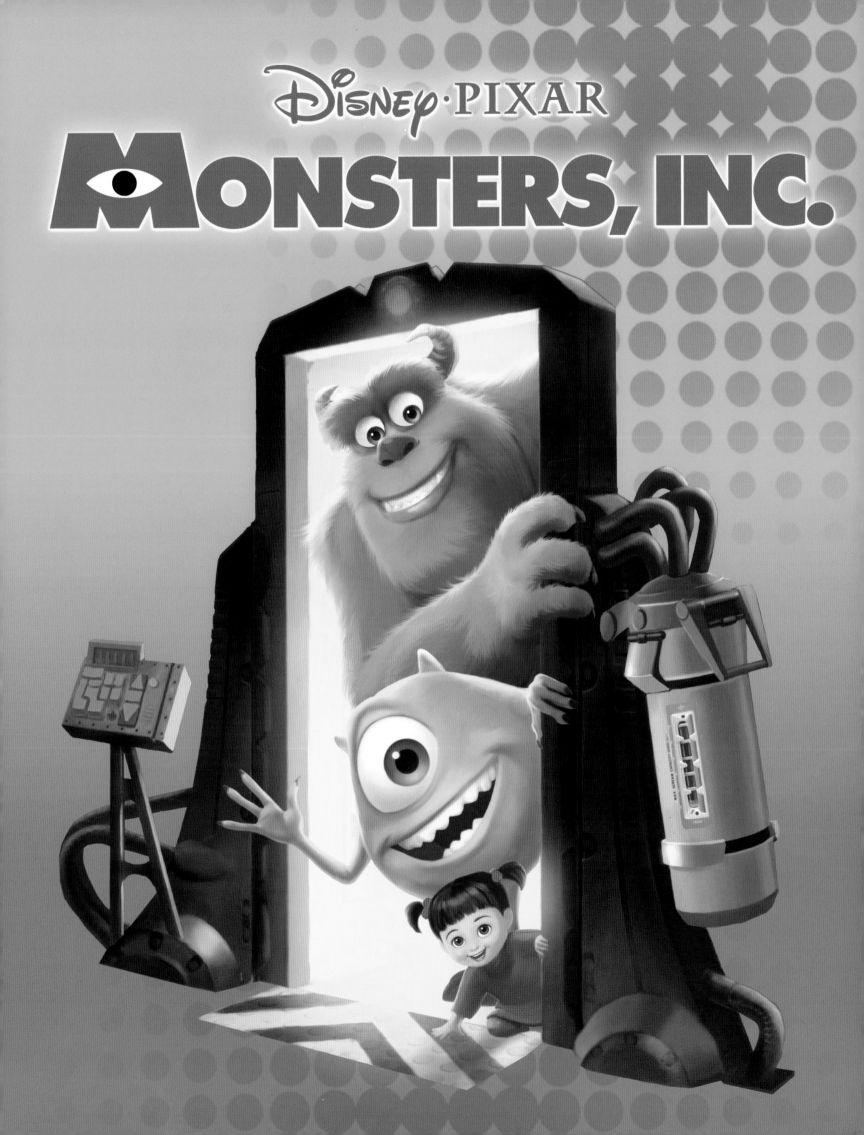

Sulley and Mike are good citizens because they are walking to work to conserve scream energy. Maybe some of the other monsters should walk to work, too. There is a lot of traffic. Can you find these vehicles?

Mike's car

Snarley-Davidson

Yeller Cab

Octocycle

I-Scream Truck

Dragon Racer

Wretch Limo

Ghoulsmobile

Welcome to Monsters, Inc. Today is *Bring Your Little Monster to Work Day,* but things are not really working out that well. Lots of the kids are separated from their parents. Can you find and match each lost kid to the correct parent?

Tyler

Tiffany

Cole

Ashley

Brandon

Brittney

Jennifer

Alexander

This is the Scare Floor, and the monsters are preparing to scare. Everyone is trying to be very frightening, but even monsters need a little help sometimes. Can you find these scary things for the monsters to use?

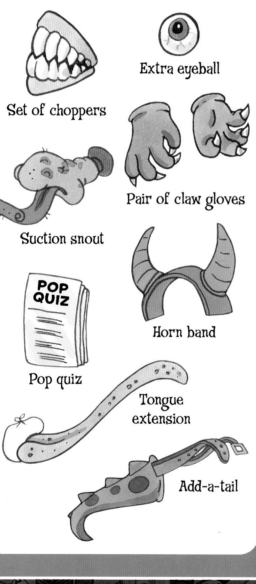

Set of choppers

Extra eyeball

Suction snout

Pair of claw gloves

Pop quiz

Horn band

Tongue extension

Add-a-tail

It's chaos at Harryhausen's. Boo may be small, but she is causing a lot of trouble. Everyone has seen her, and everyone is scared. Look for these very important monsters in the scene.

Mayor of Monstropolis

Miss Monstropolis

Fluffy Poodlepuff

Anchorman

Ellington Kingsley Poodlepuff, IV

Major Catastrophe

Jean-Pierre LeScare

Dr. Ringworm

Sulley and Mike manage to get Boo back to their apartment. They aren't quite sure what to do with her, but she seems to have her own ideas. She is contaminating all of Mike's stuff, and it is driving him crazy. Find Mike's *former* favorite things.

Sunglass

Book

Calendar

Mug

Chair

Teddy bear

Pizza box

Baseball cap

So many doors and so little time!
Sulley and Mike don't know whether
they are coming or going, but they
must find Boo before Randall does.
While you help them look, can you
also find the closet doors that
belong to these kids?

Boo

Jenna

Caleb

Tim

Louis

Rayna

Lily

Ginger

This is the new Laugh Floor, and the monsters are going about things a little differently. They are having lots of fun, but it is still hard work. Not everyone is a comedian. Lend a hand by finding these funny things for the monsters to use.

Squirting flower

Can of nuts

nuts

Whoopee cushion

Pie for throwing

Banana peel

Pair of funny glasses

Clown nose

Trick arrow

We've been Andy's toys for years.
Now that he's going to college,
what's going to happen to us?

Andy will soon be going away to college. He hasn't played with his toys in a long time. When he packs up his boxes, he will bring these things instead.

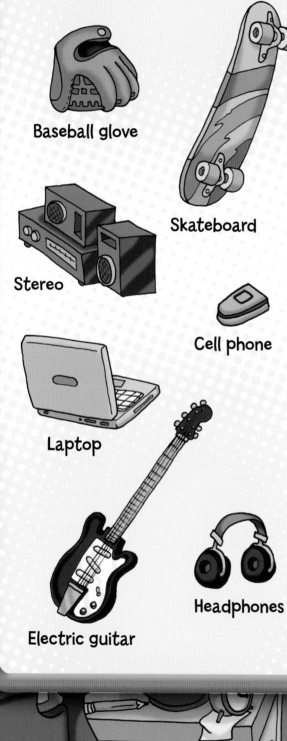

Baseball glove

Skateboard

Stereo

Cell phone

Laptop

Electric guitar

Headphones

When Andy's toys are donated to Sunnyside Daycare, Lotso assures them that their worries are over. The toys believe it — the Butterfly Room looks like toy heaven! Look around for these other toys that call Sunnyside home.

**Toy truck**

**Stretch**

**Sparks**

**Big Baby**

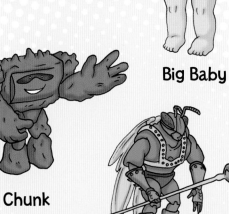

**Chunk**

**Twitch**

The Caterpillar Room isn't as fun as the toys thought it would be! Search for these toys that might be better for the little kids to play with.

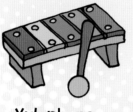

Xylophone

Plastic frying pan

Wooden blocks

Big plastic keys

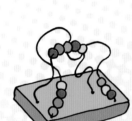

"Roller coaster" toy

Toy lawn mower

Big bouncy ball

Bonnie finds Woody outside of Sunnyside and decides to take him home. She introduces Woody to her other toys and serves them all lunch. Find these colorful items from Bonnie's kitchen set.

Purple teapot

Blue teacup

Pink plate

Yellow bowl

Red tumbler

Green pitcher

Lotso's guards won't let the toys leave the Caterpillar Room. But the guards don't know that Woody has returned to rescue his friends! They don't belong in the storage bins. Find these art supplies that do.

**Bundle of pipe cleaners**

**Jar of paint**

**Safety scissors**

**Glue**

**Paintbrush**

**Jar of glitter**

**Box of crayons**

Woody helped his friends escape from the Caterpillar Room. Now they just have to make it across the playground without being spotted by one of the guards. Search the playground to see where they've hidden!

This alien

Rex

Jessie

Slinky Dog

Bullseye

Woody

Hamm

Buzz

The toys escape Sunnyside in a garbage truck, and the truck dumps them in a landfill. Ending up here is every toy's greatest fear! Hunt for these broken toys that Woody and his friends see.

Headless doll

Action figure

Toy truck

Stuffed panda

Football

Toy horse

When Woody realizes that Andy will never forget him, he decides that all the toys should stick together...at Bonnie's house! Look around the yard to find these toys that already live there.

Peas-in-a-Pod

Mr. Pricklepants

Buttercup

Trixie

Chuckles

Dolly

Race back to Doc's garage to find the three Piston Cups that he won.

Mosey back to Mater's junkyard to find these car parts that are in the wrong piles.

- ❏ Muffler
- ❏ Tire
- ❏ Wheel
- ❏ Bumper
- ❏ Spring
- ❏ Axle

Go back to the submarine with Bruce and his vegetarian friends. Over the years, many divers have tried to explore the sunken sub, but for some reason they can't get out of there fast enough! Can you spot the things the divers left behind?

- ❏ Diver's fin
- ❏ Diver's mask
- ❏ Underwater flashlight
- ❏ Underwater camera
- ❏ Weight belt
- ❏ Scuba tank

The rest of the Tank Gang escaped the fish tank, as well! Go back to the last scene in the ocean and look for them.

Gill

Bloat

Gurgle

Bubbles

Jacques

Peach

Deb (and Flo)

Go back to Nemo's escape from Dr. Sherman's exam room and look for Darla's birthday presents.

- ❏ A doll
- ❏ A beach ball
- ❏ Nemo
- ❏ A pair of swim fins
- ❏ A baton
- ❏ A pair of roller skates